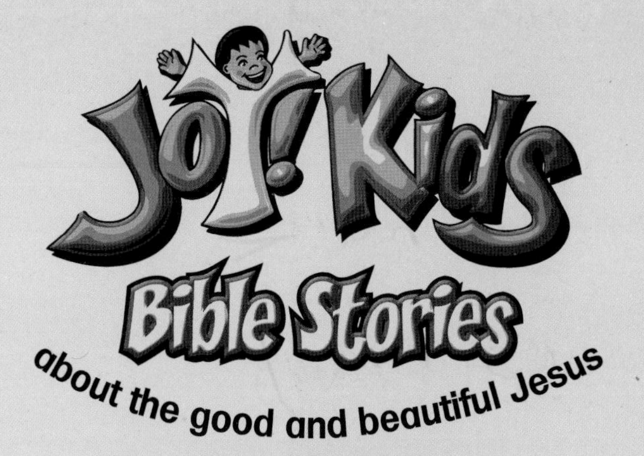

about the good and beautiful Jesus

Written by Ewald van Rensburg
Illustrations by Lilani Brits

Kids celebrate loving Jesus!

1. The wise men

(Matthew 2:1-23)

Some wise men rode on camels from a faraway land. They were following a bright star. This star told them that a special King had been born to the world.

The bright star led the wise men to Bethlehem. It stopped above a house, and there they found God's Son, Jesus, with His mother, Mary.

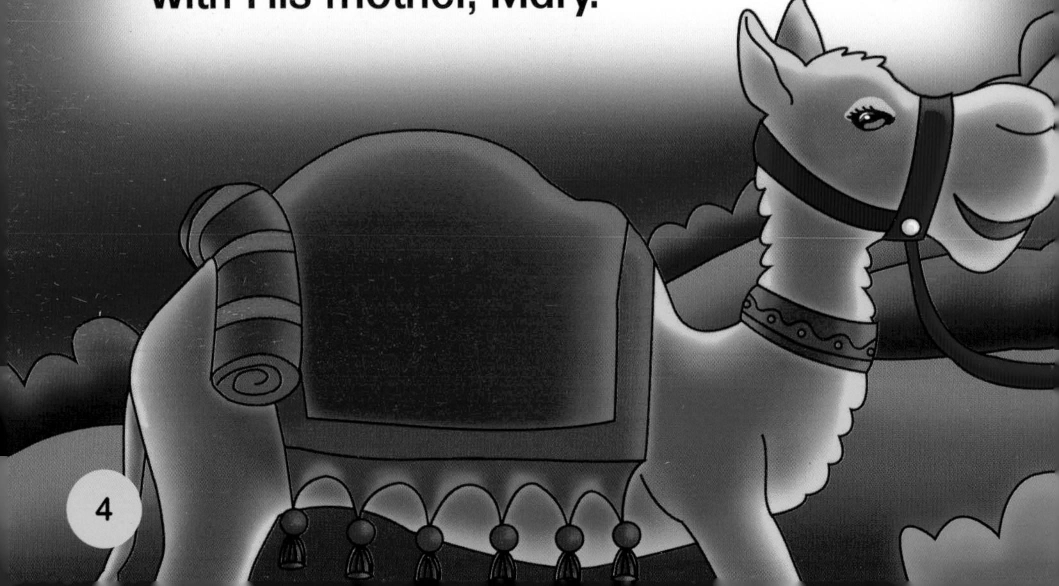

The wise men gave Jesus lovely, expensive presents of gold, frankincense and myrrh.

Then they went back home feeling very happy because they had seen Jesus, the King of the world, at last.

Come, let's pray together:

Jesus, You are the greatest King in the world. Amen

Remember every day to give your best to Jesus, just like the wise men did.

2. Jesus is baptised

(Matthew 3)

God sent John the Baptist to tell the people that Jesus was coming. John also told them they had to love God.

One day John was standing in the river telling a crowd of people that God's special One was coming soon.

Suddenly John noticed Jesus standing in the crowd. He was so excited; he told everyone that Jesus was God's special One!

Jesus walked into the river so that John could baptise Him.

Then God spoke from heaven and everyone heard Him say: “This is My Son and I love Him very much. You must listen to Him and obey Him!”

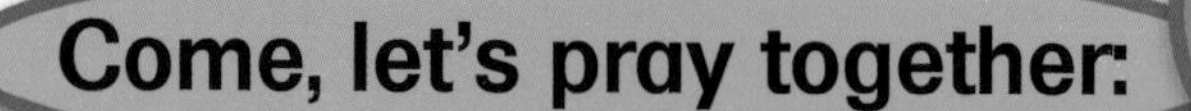

Jesus, I will always listen to You and obey You. Amen

God also says to you: “You are My child and I love you very much!”

3. Jesus looks after us

(Matthew 6:25-34)

One day Jesus was telling His disciples and a crowd of other people how God's people should live.

He saw some birds flying in the sky and asked the people, "Do you see those birds flying up there?" Everyone looked up and nodded their heads. "Our Father God looks after all the birds. He gives them food to eat. Remember God loves you, His children, even more than those birds. So you must never be worried. He will give you everything you need."

Come, let's pray together:

Jesus, thank You for always giving me everything I need. Amen

God looks after the grass, the flowers and the birds. He also looks after you.

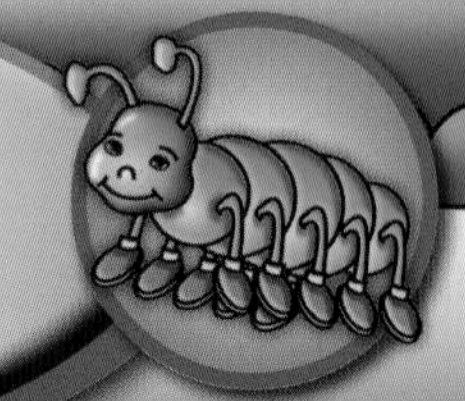

4. Jesus loves little children very much (Mark 10:13-16)

One day, a group of mothers brought their children to see Jesus. They wanted Jesus to bless their children.

Jesus' disciples shouted at them to leave Him alone. But Jesus told His disciples not to chase the mothers and children away. His followers should have known by then that Jesus loved children very much.

Then all the children laughed and ran up to Jesus. He hugged them, stroked their hair, put His hands on their heads and told them they were special.

Come, let's pray together:

Jesus, thank You that You have a special place in Your heart for children. Amen

Children like you are very special to Jesus. He loves you very much.

5. Jesus is coming back

(Revelation 21)

At the moment Jesus lives in a wonderful place called Heaven, but one day He will come back. He made this promise to us; and Jesus always keeps His promises.

When He comes back, Jesus will make everything on earth brand new. It's going to be the best place ever. The trees will have fruit all year round and it will always be summertime. We will be very happy and no one will be sad again. The most wonderful news is that we will be with Jesus forever and ever. This is something to look forward to!

Remember, when Jesus promises something, He always keeps His promises.

Come, let's pray together:
Jesus, I'm so glad that You are coming back one day to make the whole world brand new.
Amen

Guidelines for parents

Faith Icon
The formation of faith is indeed unique to each child; there are however general characteristics that apply to all children. There are three main ways in which children develop faith:

- Parents regularly reading the Bible, telling Bible and other faith based stories, praying together and doing faith building activities with their children (such as the ones found in this book).
- Children ask questions – parents need to take these questions seriously and answer them according to the child's level of understanding.
- Children follow the example of those caring for them.

Emotional Intelligence Icon
We experience emotions long before we learn the language that enables us to express how we are feeling. Therefore it is important for children to be taught how to verbalise what they are feeling. Use the illustrations accompanying the stories and ask your child how they think the people or animals in the picture feel. This helps them become aware of their own emotions as well as those of others. It provides a learning opportunity where the child can learn appropriate words to express how they are feeling.

Reading Icon
A wonderful world opens up for your child when they start learning to read. Enjoy every moment of this exciting adventure with your child. Let them sit on your lap where they can be comfortable and feel safe and secure. Open the book holding it so that you can both see the pages. Read clearly and with enthusiasm. As you know you can read the same story over and over. Point out where you are reading with your finger as you go along. This will help your child to begin to see the relationship between letters, sounds, words and their meaning. Encourage your child's attempts at reading – even if it sounds like gibberish.

Listening Skills Icon
Listening is an important learning and developmental skill. You can help develop this skill in your child by encouraging them to listen attentively, and understand what they are hearing. Let them look at the illustrations and then use their imagination to tell the story back to you in their own words. You can also encourage them to do this by asking questions relating to the story. Yet another way is to leave out words from a story the child knows well and let them fill in the missing words.

Vocabulary Icon
Use every opportunity to build your child's vocabulary – this is a lifelong gift that you are giving to them. Start with everyday objects and people in the illustrations in books. Point at the picture, say the word, form a short sentence using the word. Repeat it again and then let your child say the word. Try to use the word in another context – if there is a tent in the picture you are looking at then say: we sleep in a tent when we go camping.

Numeracy Skills Icon
It is important for your child to develop numeracy skills. Play simple games such as: "How many ducks are there in the picture? If we add two more ducks how many are there now? Then if three fly away? (use your fingers to illustrate this) How many are left?" They also need to recognise the shape of numbers – cut large numbers from cardboard – let your child play with these – place the numbers in order forming a line from one to ten.